KT-465-770

00006260

This book is to be return...
the last date stamp...

HUMPHREY PERKINS
HIGH SCHOOL

00006260

MEASURING AND MAPS

Design	David West
	Children's Book Design
Editorial Planning	Clark Robinson Limited
Picture Researcher	Emma Krikler
Illustrator	Ian Moores
Consultant	Elizabeth Turner,
	Department of Geography
	Stamford High School

© Aladdin Books 1991
Designed and produced by
Aladdin Books Ltd
28 Percy Street
London W1P 9FF

First published in
Great Britain in 1991 by
Franklin Watts
96 Leonard Street
London EC2A 4RH

ISBN 0-7496-0595-2

A CIP catalogue record for this book is
available from the British Library.

All rights reserved

Printed in Belgium

HANDS · ON · GEOGRAPHY
MEASURING AND MAPS

KEITH LYE

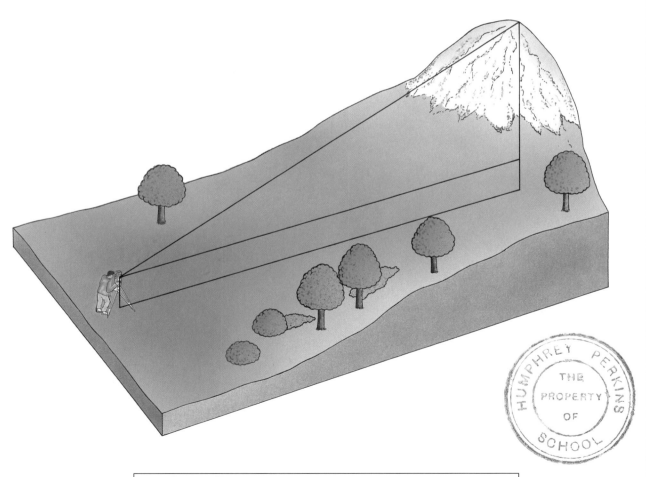

HUMPHREY PERKINS THE PROPERTY OF SCHOOL

GLOUCESTER PRESS
London · New York · Toronto · Sydney

CONTENTS

This book is about maps — from globes that show the whole Earth to maps that show just a small area of land. It tells you how to understand maps, how people take measurements to make maps, and about methods people use to find their position. There are "hands on" projects to try which use everyday items as equipment. There are also "did you know?" panels of information for fun.

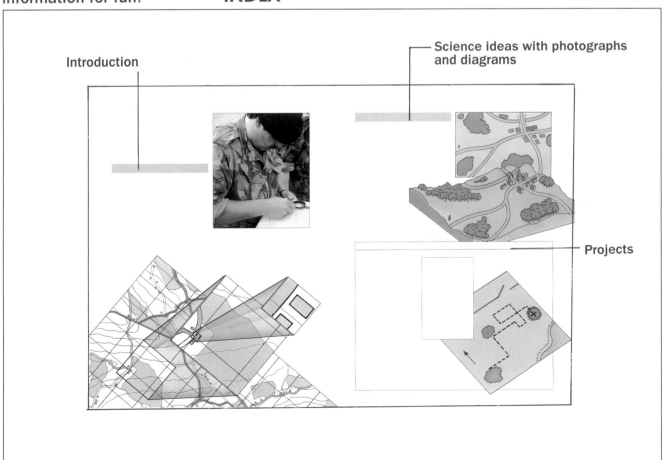

Introduction

Science ideas with photographs and diagrams

Projects

Maps are ways of portraying the Earth, or a part of it, on a flat surface — usually a sheet of paper. Maps are similar to photographs taken from aircraft or spacecraft. But photographs give far less information than maps do. For example, map-makers use colours, symbols, words and numbers to show hills and valleys, the heights of mountains, and the names of places and land features. There are none of these things on air photographs.

General reference maps give information about a whole continent, a single country or a particular region. They show two main kinds of feature. First, they indicate such natural features as rivers, forests and the height of land. Second, they show things made by people, such as cities, roads and boundaries. Special maps concentrate on one feature, such as rainfall or rail routes. Books of maps are called atlases.

Models of the ground hanging above a huge aerial photograph.

Space photographs show that the Earth is shaped like a ball and that its surface is curved. The curvature limits the distance you can see towards the horizon — the line where the Earth and the sky seem to meet. At sea level, the horizon is about four kilometres away, although a person on the top of a mountain can see farther.

GLOBES

Because maps are flat and the Earth's surface is curved, the only true way of showing of the world is a globe. Globes are hollow spheres made of cardboard, metal or plastic. Land features may be printed on strips of paper, which are pasted onto the surface of the globe.

Globes show the true shapes, areas and positions of continents and the oceans. But such features are often distorted on flat maps. For example, the shortest distance between two places on a world map seems to be the straight line joining them. But if you use a piece of string to join the same two places on a globe, you will find that the shortest path is a curved line that follows a different route. This curved line is part of a great circle — a line that goes right round the Earth, dividing it into two equal parts. For example, the Equator, an imaginary line that lies half-way between the North and South Poles, is a great circle. Even so, globes have disadvantages. Their size and shape make them difficult to carry around, whereas a map can be folded and carried in a pocket.

▷ Some globes are fixed and cannot be moved. Others are mounted on stands so that you can turn them around on their axes, which are usually tilted by 23.5 degrees. This is the same tilt as the Earth's axis (the line that joins the North Pole, the centre of the Earth and the South Pole). By rotating the globe you get a series of views of the Earth.

▷ The diagram shows the Equator (0 degrees latitude), the Tropic of Cancer (about 23.5 degrees North), the Tropic of Capricorn (about 23.5 degrees South) and the prime meridian (0 degrees longitude).

Longitude

Latitude

Prime meridian

Equator

Tropic of Capricorn

Tropic of Cancer

LINES ON THE GLOBE

Lines of latitude (or parallels) are lines on globes that run parallel to the Equator. Running at right angles to the parallels are lines of longitude, or meridians. Lines of latitude and longitude are measured in degrees. For example, the North Pole has a latitude of 90 degrees North, the Equator is latitude 0 degrees, and the South Pole is 90 degrees South. Meridians are measured 180 degrees East and West of the prime meridian, which runs through Greenwich, London.

◁ A network of lines of latitude and longitude cover the globe. Map-makers use this grid, or graticule, to draw maps. Every place on Earth has its own latitude and longitude.

DID YOU KNOW?

The Earth is slightly flattened at the poles and it bulges near the Equator. The distance through the Earth from the North to South Poles is 12,713 kilometres. The diameter of the Earth at the Equator is slightly larger: 12,756.3 kilometres. This shape is described as an oblate spheroid.

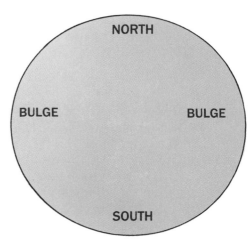

NORTH

BULGE

BULGE

SOUTH

8 MAP SCALES

Scales on maps are sometimes shown as ratios or fractions, such as 1:50,000. This means that 1 centimetre on the map represents 50,000 centimetres (0.5 kilometres) on the ground. Some maps have scales in words and figures, such as 1 centimetre = 15 kilometres. Others have scale bars showing distances.

LARGE SCALES

Maps drawn to a large scale cover only a small area. Some large-scale maps are called plans. For example, a large-scale map might show a street, with each house marked on it. An even larger scale might show gardens and even individual trees. A garden measuring 20 metres long and 10 metres wide might be drawn on a plan at a scale of 1 centimetre = 1 metre (making it 20 centimetres by 10 centimetres on the plan). Expressed as a ratio, this scale would be 1:100.

SMALL SCALES

Small scales are used for maps that cover large areas. For example, a one-page map of North America in an atlas might be drawn at the small scale of 1:35,000,000, or 1 centimetre = 350 kilometres. This map would show the countries, states, counties or provinces, and the positions of major cities. But if you want to learn more about California, you must look at the map of just this state, which might be drawn at a larger scale of 1:2,500,000, or 1 centimetre = 25 kilometres. If you want information about the city of Los Angeles, you must turn to the city map, which might have an even larger scale of 1:30,000.

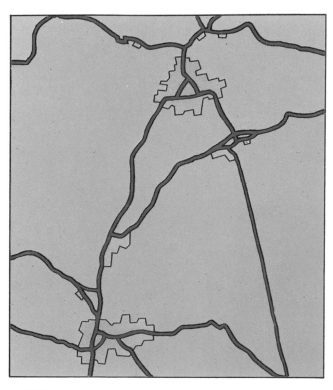

△ This made-up small-scale map shows only main roads, cities, towns and villages. It shows a very large area.

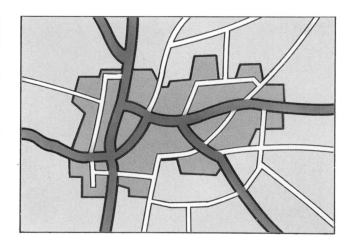

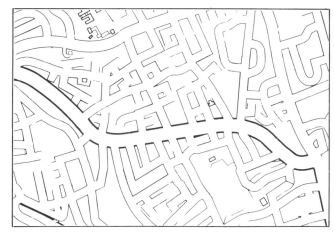

▷ The middle map is at a larger scale than the top map. It shows more detail, such as smaller roads. The bottom map is at a large scale. It shows every street.

MAPS WITHOUT SCALES

Some special maps are not drawn to scale and deliberately distort directions and the positions of places. For example, some cities produce maps of this kind showing the routes on their complex underground railway systems. An accurate map showing the precise positions of all stations would confuse travellers. Instead, map-makers simplify the maps, making most of the railway lines appear to be straight, and making the distances between stations appear the same. Such simplified maps are easy to use.

LRT Registered User No. 91/1366

△ London's underground railway system can be shown on an easy-to-use map which is not drawn to scale.

SCALE MAP OF A GARDEN

A garden 150 paces long and 100 paces wide appears on the plan, at a scale of 1:10, as a rectangle 15 centimetres long and 10 centimetres wide. To show the position of a tree, pace out the distance along one side of the garden until you are facing the tree at right angles. Pace the distance from the side to the tree and mark the distances on the plan at the correct scale.

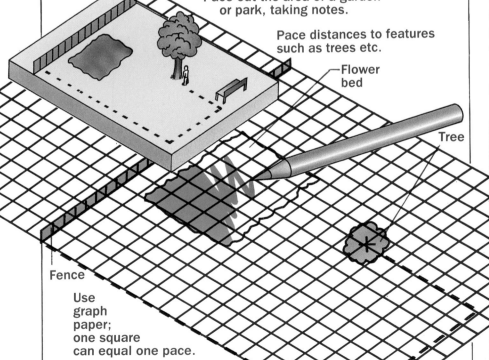

Pace out the area of a garden or park, taking notes.

Pace distances to features such as trees etc.

Flower bed

Tree

Fence

Use graph paper; one square can equal one pace.

DID YOU KNOW?

Why did the explorer Christopher Columbus call the people of America Indians? When he sailed west from Spain, he used a map drawn at the wrong scale, making the world seem smaller than it is. He thought he had reached India but, in fact, he had reached the West Indies.

If you want to walk across country between two places, you can find out the distance from an accurate map. Before you set out, you also need to know the direction in which you should travel. All maps show directions. On most maps, north is at the top. On atlas maps, lines of latitude and longitude show directions.

COMPASS POINTS

The eight main points (or directions) of the compass are north, north-east, east, south-east, south, south-west, west, and north-west. Many compasses show 16 or even 32 points.

A small magnetic compass, which fits in your pocket, is a simple way of finding directions. The needle of a compass points to the magnetic North Pole, which is near the geographic (or true) North Pole. The difference in direction between the two poles is often shown (in degrees) in the margin of maps. If you stand facing due north, you know that south is directly behind you. West is at right angles on your left, and east is on your right.

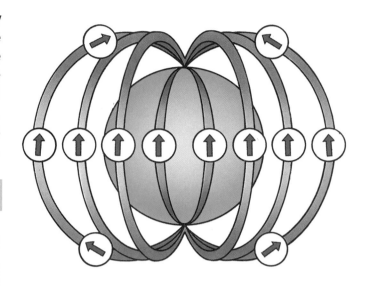

△ A compass always points north along the lines of Earth's magnetic field.

▽ When you have found north with a magnetic compass, you can line up, or orientate, the map. This helps you to find out where you are.

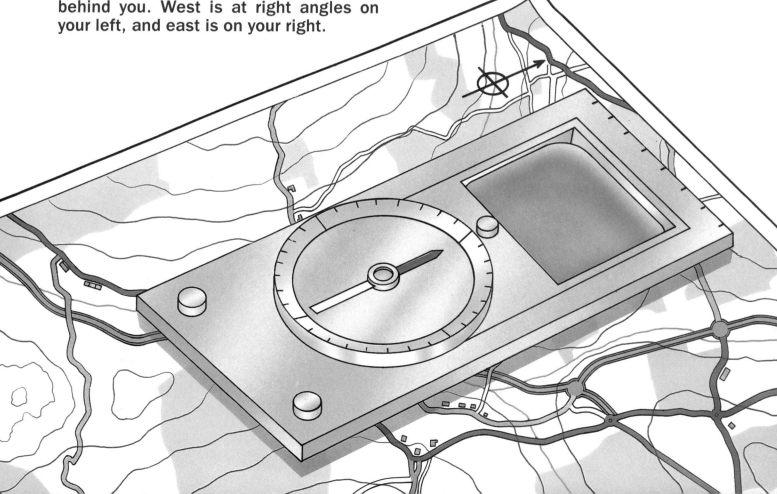

FOLLOW A STAR

On a clear night in the Northern Hemisphere, you can find out where north is located by facing Polaris, which is also called the Pole Star or the North Star.

Polaris is the brightest star in the constellation of Ursa Minor, which is also known as the Little Bear or the Little Dipper. Polaris is located almost directly above the North Pole and it appears to remain almost stationary, while the other stars gradually turn around in the sky. For several thousand years, navigators have used Polaris to find their way across seas and oceans at night.

▷ The constellation Ursa Major (or the Great Bear) resembles a saucepan. The line joining the two stars at the front of the pan points to Polaris.

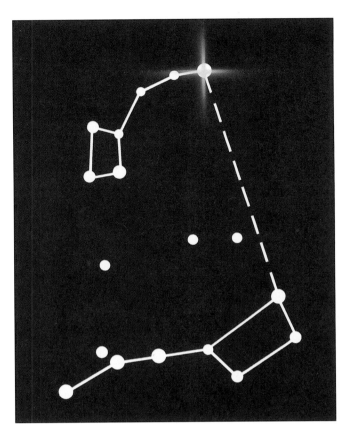

MAPPING DIRECTIONS

The diagram shows the directions that a person must take to walk from home to school. The compass shows the direction of north. Coming out of the house, the person would have to turn east, which is at right angles to north. The road then turns north-east and then east before reaching a crossroads. Beyond the crossroads, the person has to follow roads running south, south-east and east. The final part of the journey leads the walker north, north-east and north.

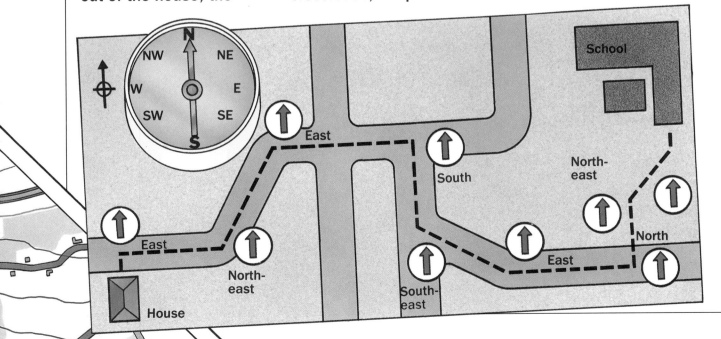

To pack as much information as possible on a map, map-makers use a kind of shorthand. For example, a blue line indicates a river and a blue area a lake or sea. A red line may indicate a main road, and a group of tiny drawings of trees indicates a forest. These are all types of map symbol.

SYMBOLS AND SCALES

The amount of information on a map depends on the scale. The finest line that can be drawn on a map is 0.005 centimetres thick. On a map with a scale of 1:1,000,000, this width represents 50 metres. As a result, a main road can be shown only as a thin red line. But on a scale of 1:50,000, which is used on many topographic maps, a road can be made more prominent and shown as a red line between two black ones. Scale also limits information about such features as cities. On an atlas map, a large city may be indicated by a black square or circle. On a large-scale map, the shape of the city can be shown.

UPS AND DOWNS

Map-makers use several methods to show relief (differences in height on the Earth's surface). High mountain peaks appear as spot heights, which give the precise height of a mountain.

Other methods are needed to show the ups and downs of the land. This can be done by using contours – lines that join places with the same height. Shading is sometimes used for rocky areas to create a three-dimensional effect. Atlas-makers often use layer tints (a series of colours) to show various levels. Sometimes, layer tinting and hill shading are combined. Coloured models of the land are lit so that the hills cast shadows. The model is photographed and the picture used to create the effect of relief on the map.

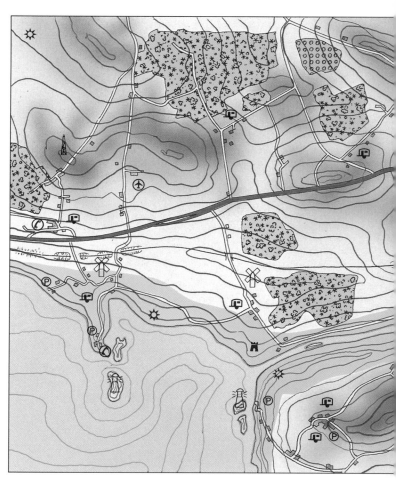

▽ The ups and downs of the land can be shown by hill shading. Another method uses contours, which join together points of equal height.

Shadow projection

Contours

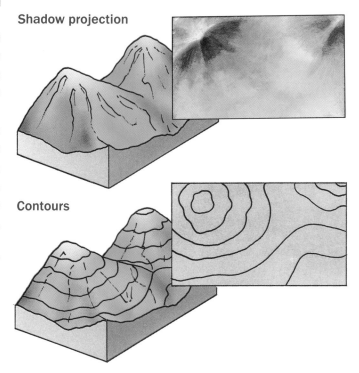

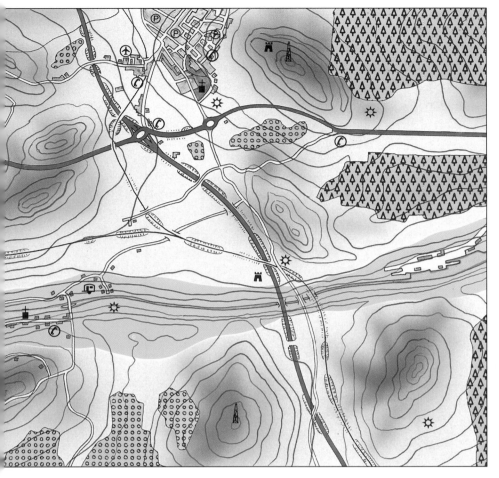

KEY

⊕ Airport

✆ Telephone

♜ Castle

⚲ TV or radio mast

✳ Windmill

✝ Church

✺ Ancient site

Ⓟ Car park

🚐 Caravan site

🗼 Lighthouse

◁ Topographic maps use symbols which are shown in legends (keys). Some examples of symbols are shown above.

MAKE YOUR OWN MAP SYMBOLS

Draw a rough map of the area around your home. You will find many features, such as lamp posts, post boxes, public telephones and traffic lights, to put on your map as symbols. When making symbols, remember that they should be simple and easy to draw, but they should also give an impression of the feature concerned.

Draw a simple map

Some possible symbols

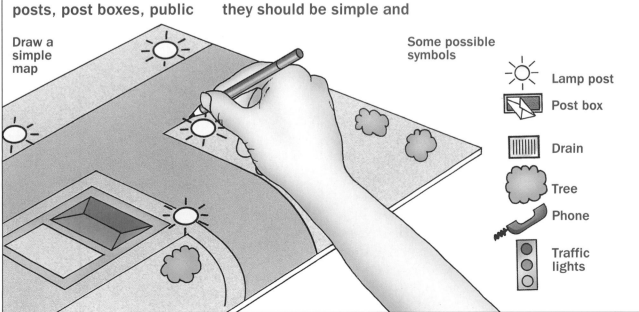

Lamp post

Post box

Drain

Tree

Phone

Traffic lights

The amount of information map-makers can show about an area is limited by the scale and the space available. Special maps give information about one aspect of an area. Almost anything can be shown on special, or thematic, maps such as physical maps, political maps, population maps and vegetation maps.

PHYSICAL AND POLITICAL

Physical, or relief, maps show the physical features of the land, including mountains, plains, rivers and lakes. Physical maps in atlases often use green and yellow tints to indicate low-lying areas. Browns, reds and purples are used for high areas, and the highest peaks are often coloured white. The names on these maps identify the main physical features, natural regions, islands and the seas and oceans.

Physical maps do not show cultural (human) features, which appear on political maps. The boundaries of countries and smaller divisions, such as states, provinces, counties and other areas, together with political capitals, are shown on political maps. Colours help to distinguish political divisions.

UNDER THE SEA

Water covers about seven-tenths of the Earth's surface but, until recently, little was known about the ocean bed. Most people assumed that it was a vast, featureless plain.

But in the 1920s, instruments called echo-sounders came into use. These instruments enabled ships to measure the depth of the water as they sailed along. Since the 1940s, echo-sounders have been used to map most of the ocean floor (see page 21). The maps show that the physical features on the ocean floor are as varied as those on land. They have also shed light on the Earth sciences.

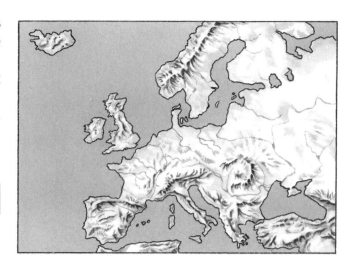

△ Physical maps show land features, such as mountains.

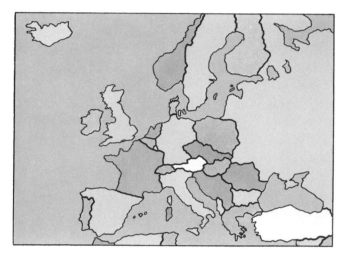

△ Political maps show human features, such as countries.

△ Recent maps of the ocean floor show that it contains mountain ranges, volcanic peaks (some forming islands), trenches and broad plains.

RAINFALL MAPS

Some special maps show the amount of rain that falls in different parts of a region each year. They usually use darker shades for areas with heavy rainfall and lighter shades for areas that have little rain. Comparing rainfall maps to physical maps shows how physical features affect the weather. For example, it often rains more on hills and mountains.

▽ The rainfall map of Europe shows a lot of rain on the coasts of the ocean and on high areas. It also shows little rainfall where it is very hot or very cold.

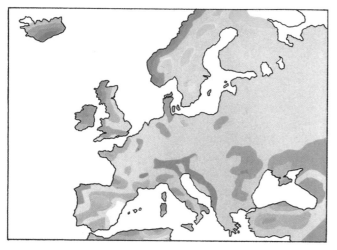

VEGETATION MAPS

Some maps show the plants that grow in various regions. Some vegetation maps use tints to distinguish between vegetation regions. Others contain tiny drawings, or pictograms, to show the main plant types. Comparing these maps to physical and rainfall maps, you can find out the conditions that produce various kinds of plant life.

▽ The vegetation map of Europe shows how the plant life varies between the cold regions in the north and on mountains, and the much warmer lands in the south.

DID YOU KNOW?

From Earth, we can only ever see one side of the Moon. The features on the far side were unknown until the space age. Between 1966 and 1967, five Orbiter spacecraft took photographs of almost the entire surface of the Moon, thus revealing the landscape of the far side of the Moon. This map (on the right) includes details of the spacecraft that have landed there.

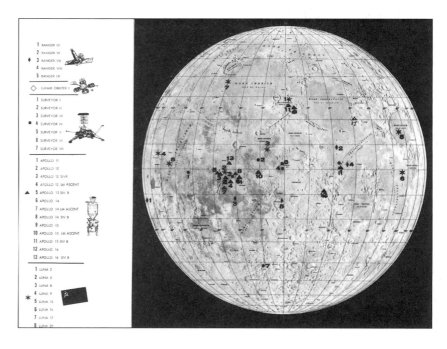

General reference maps have many uses. They are essential tools for travellers, navigators, members of the armed forces, town planners, and so on. The amount of information you can get from a map depends on your ability to read the map. First, you must be able to find places and discover where you are.

FINDING PLACES

Most atlases contain indexes, which list the names of places. Next to each name is a map page number and the latitude and longitude of the place. By knowing the latitude and longitude, map-users can pinpoint the place exactly.

Some maps are divided into squares which are labelled either in numbers, as on many topographic maps, or in letters and numbers. For example, the key to the map may say that a town is in square B4. The system of letters and numbers is used in city street atlases.

△ Members of the armed forces frequently use maps.

▽ Map grids (networks of squares) locate places. Finding a grid reference is like "zooming in" on an area.

WHERE ARE YOU?

Hikers often use maps to find their way around. They learn how to pick out land features and identify the symbols that portray these features on their map. By taking bearings from the features with a magnetic compass, they can work out their position on the map. They can also find their position fairly accurately without a compass, simply by judging the distance to the features.

▷ A walker identifies land features, such as villages and bridges. By finding these on a map, the walker can judge where he or she is standing.

HUNTING FOR TREASURE

Pirates once hid their booty on tropical islands. They drew rough maps, showing prominent features that would help them to find the spot again years later. You can make a treasure map in a local park. First, make a rough map of the park and draw on an arrow to indicate north. Now plan a route to the spot where the treasure is buried. You must give instructions on where to start the search. Then note down the directions and distances involved in reaching the spot. See whether your friends can find the "treasure" using your map.

Instructions
from bush:
5 paces East
4 paces North
5 paces East
2 paces South
2 paces East
5 paces North
4 paces West
3 paces South
6 paces East
2 paces South

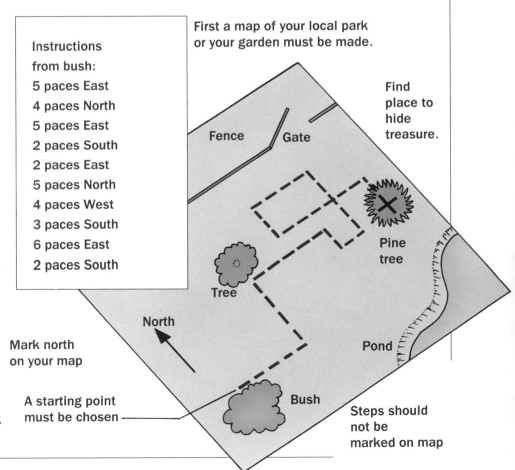

First a map of your local park or your garden must be made.

Find place to hide treasure.

Fence   Gate

Pine tree

Tree

North

Pond

Mark north on your map

A starting point must be chosen

Bush

Steps should not be marked on map

People who measure the land are called land surveyors. The mapping of an area begins by creating a network of points and measuring the distances and angles between them. The second stage is to map all the details of the land, such as rivers, roads, and so on, between the accurately fixed points in the network.

TRIANGULATION

The first step in a survey is to measure the distance between two points, several kilometres apart. This distance is called the base line. Traditionally, measuring a base line is done using metal tapes.

Next, the surveyor measures the angles between the two points at the end of the base line and a third point, using a telescopic instrument, called a theodolite. The three points form a triangle and, if you know the length of one side of a triangle and all three angles, you can calculate the length of the other two sides. The surveyor then continues to fix the positions of other points in a network of triangles by angular measurements alone. This method of surveying is called triangulation.

△ Surveyors use plane tables to measure details of the land.

▽ To map an area, surveyors measure a base line (B-C) and fix a third point (A) by angular measurements. Other points (F, E, D, and so on) are fixed by measuring angles.

Known fixed points are plotted on paper at a chosen scale, and measured height and depressions are drawn in.

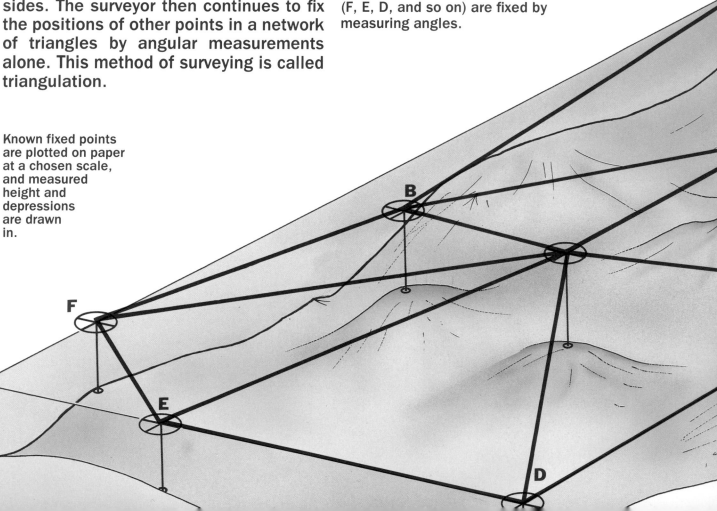

DETAILED MAPPING

Until the 1950s, the main method of measuring the details of the land between the fixed points was plane table surveying. Today this has been replaced by mapping from air photographs.

The plane table is a flat board covered by paper, with the points fixed by triangulation plotted accurately on the surface. The board is mounted on a tripod at a known (fixed) "station". The surveyor then uses a sighting instrument, called an alidade, to measure the directions to points, such as the corners of fields. Pencil lines are drawn to these points. When the work at one station is complete, the surveyor moves on to new stations and sights the positions of points around those stations. When three sightings to the same point intersect, the point is then fixed. Gradually, the spaces between the fixed points are filled in.

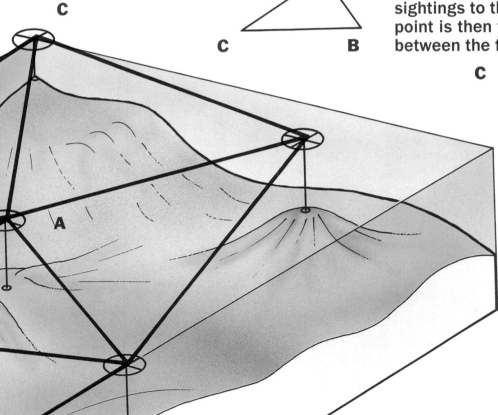

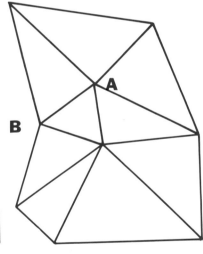

DID YOU KNOW?

Measuring a base line with metal tapes is a slow job. Surveyors can now measure distances quickly with electronic instruments that record how long it takes light or radio waves to travel between two points.

Besides measuring the details of the land, surveyors must also find out the heights of many points in the area they are mapping. From a large number of these points, they can draw in the contours that show the relief of the land. The heights are measured above mean sea level — the average level of the sea.

FIXING HEIGHTS

Accurate measurements of height are made with a surveyor's level (a telescopic instrument containing a highly sensitive spirit level). The surveyor sets up the level on a tripod over a point whose height is known. By taking a reading on a marked stick placed on a second point, the surveyor can find the height difference between the two points. Accurately fixed points are called bench marks and are cut into walls or rocks.

Surveyors also use theodolites to measure the vertical angles between two points because if you know the distance and the vertical angle between two points, you can calculate the difference in height. This method is less accurate than levelling. When it is hazy, angular measurements can be distorted.

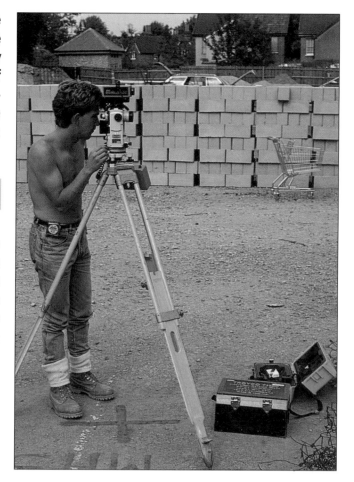

△ Land surveyors use accurate telescopic instruments called theodolites to measure horizontal and vertical angles.

▽ Surveyors measure the vertical angle between two points to work out the height difference between them. They must allow for the height of their theodolites.

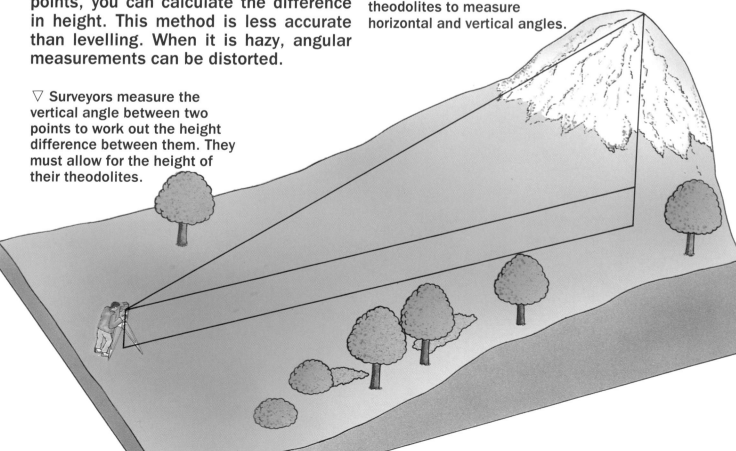

SOUNDING THE DEPTHS

Contours are used on some maps to show the depth of water along coasts. The main instrument used to find the depth of water is an echo-sounder. Echo-sounders transmit sound waves and record the echo of the wave that bounces back from the ocean floor. The speed of sound is known, and so the depth of the water can be worked out. The depths are recorded as the ship sails along.

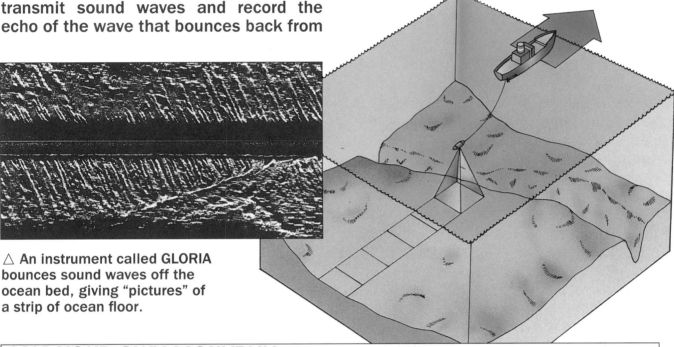

△ An instrument called GLORIA bounces sound waves off the ocean bed, giving "pictures" of a strip of ocean floor.

MAP YOUR OWN MOUNTAIN

Build a model of a mountain with clay or modelling clay on a board. Use the point of a pencil to mark rows of dots around the mountain. The dots in each row should all be at the same height. Use a ruler held vertically to make sure of this. Also, the rows should all be the same height apart — say, 3 centimetres. Now join up each row of dots with a piece of string. If you look straight down on your mountain you will see a contour map of the mountain. You could then draw a contour map on paper.

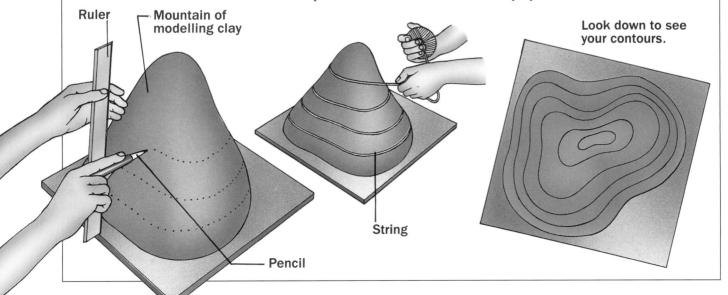

Ruler

Mountain of modelling clay

Pencil

String

Look down to see your contours.

Aerial photographs first proved useful in World Wars I and II, because they provided information about the enemy. Since World War II, they have been used for large-scale mapping and a new science called photogrammetry (making measurements from photographs) has developed.

AERIAL PHOTOGRAPHS

Aerial photographs are taken by aircraft which fly along carefully planned flight paths. They fly at a constant level and speed, taking vertical photographs — that is, pictures of the land looking directly downwards.

The cameras are specially designed to take pictures automatically at regular intervals, so that each photograph in every strip overlaps the next by about 60 per cent. When one strip of land has been photographed, the aircraft turns and photographs the next strip alongside, and overlapping, the first. Many photographs may be taken to cover a large area.

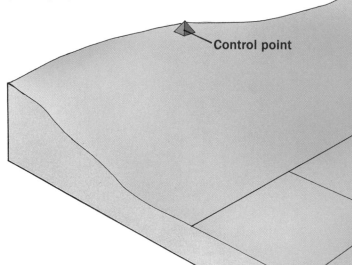

▽ Aircraft photograph the land in long strips. Points whose positions are known are identified on the photographs. They serve as control points when maps are made from the photographs.

Control point

▽ A lot of time may be spent planning a series of aerial photographs. Old maps of the area are studied (if they exist) in order to decide on the best route for the camera-carrying aircraft.

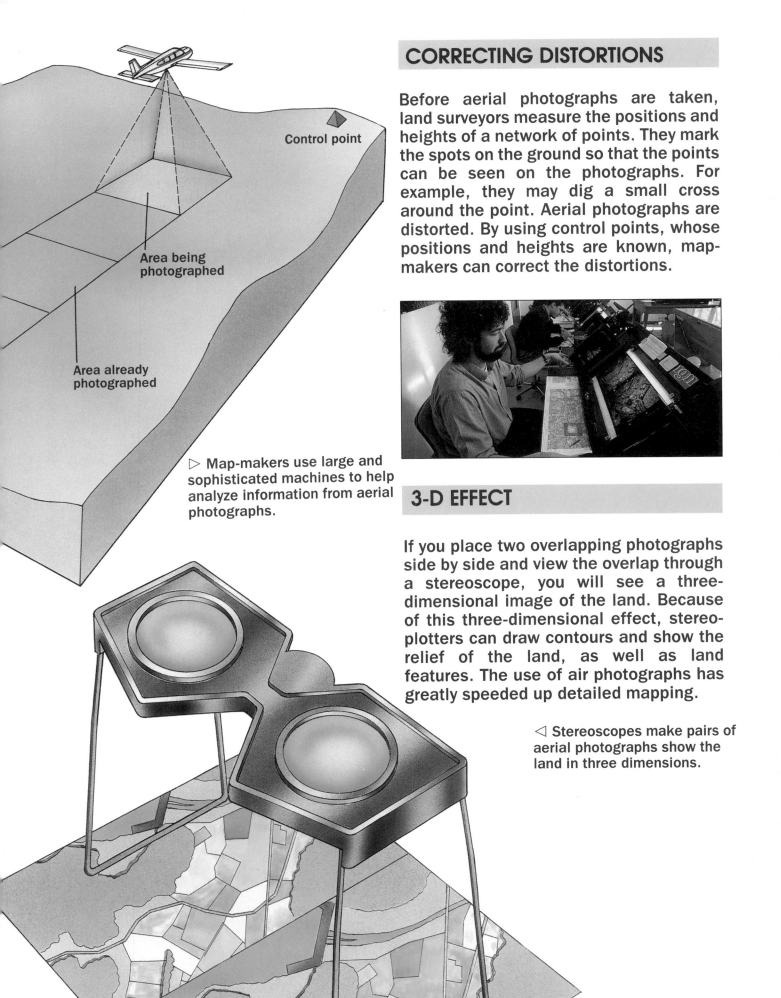

Control point

Area being
photographed

Area already
photographed

▷ Map-makers use large and
sophisticated machines to help
analyze information from aerial
photographs.

CORRECTING DISTORTIONS

Before aerial photographs are taken,
land surveyors measure the positions and
heights of a network of points. They mark
the spots on the ground so that the points
can be seen on the photographs. For
example, they may dig a small cross
around the point. Aerial photographs are
distorted. By using control points, whose
positions and heights are known, map-
makers can correct the distortions.

3-D EFFECT

If you place two overlapping photographs
side by side and view the overlap through
a stereoscope, you will see a three-
dimensional image of the land. Because
of this three-dimensional effect, stereo-
plotters can draw contours and show the
relief of the land, as well as land
features. The use of air photographs has
greatly speeded up detailed mapping.

◁ Stereoscopes make pairs of
aerial photographs show the
land in three dimensions.

In recent years, map-makers have been making increasing use of new technology, including the use of computers, especially to speed up the compilation of maps, and the use of artificial satellites to collect data for maps. Satellite photographs cover large areas. These areas can be viewed at regular intervals.

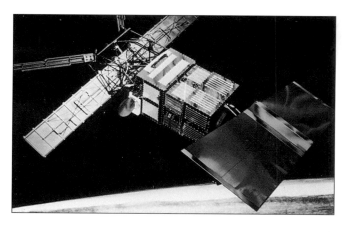

SATELLITE PHOTOGRAPHS

Measurements from satellite photographs have advanced the study of the weather and the making of maps from which weather forecasts are prepared. Satellites also employ remote sensing devices that create images of parts of the Earth to supply particular kinds of information, such as the rocks that lie on the surface. Such photographs are useful in the search for minerals. Some satellites are able to monitor conditions in the atmosphere or in the oceans.

MEASURING POINTS

Satellites greatly help geodesists (scientists who study the size and shape of the Earth). The study of the curvature of the Earth is important to map-makers who are mapping large areas.

In the last 30 years, geodesists have set up a network of points around the world whose positions are known to within one metre. They do this by a system of triangulation. Geodesists at two stations can make simultaneous measurements of the angle of a satellite. If the positions of the satellite and one station are known, they can calculate the position of the second station.

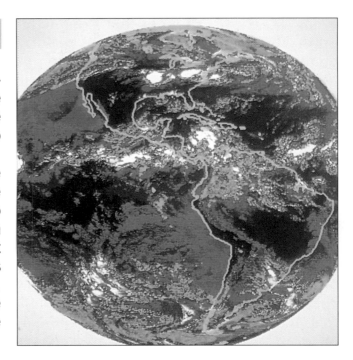

△ Satellite photographs are used to track weather formations. Regular photographs taken from space help weather forecasters to work out how the weather is behaving.

◁ Recently, a series of many photographs covering the whole of the Earth's surface has been taken by satellites. Using sophisticated modern techniques, it has been possible to join these photographs together to make one complete picture of the whole of the Earth.

DID YOU KNOW?

By the year 2000, you may be able to find your exact position within seconds. This system is based on a computer-receiver which receives signals from four satellites. The computer converts the time taken by the signals into distances and instantly works out its position.

Small areas are mapped as though the Earth is flat. But, when measuring long distances, map-makers must allow for the Earth's curvature, which makes it impossible for map-makers to draw a totally accurate map of the world. This explains why the appearance of world maps varies from one atlas to another.

ORANGE PEEL

If you peel an orange, there is no way in which you can flatten the peel without breaking it. The same applies to the curved surface of the Earth. As a result, map-makers use map projections which ensure that some map features, such as areas or distances, are true. But no world map can show all features accurately.

Most projections are worked out by mathematics. But they can be understood if you imagine that the globe is made of glass, with a light at its centre.

▷ An interrupted projection shows strips of the Earth's surface, like those that globe-makers use. But as a world map, it is not very useful.

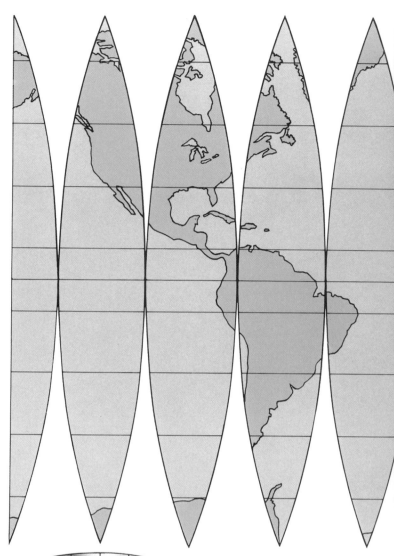

PROJECTIONS

A cylindrical projection is formed by wrapping a piece of paper around a globe, touching it along the Equator. The light casts shadows of the graticule on to the paper. The length of the Equator is the same on the cylinder as it is on the globe. But other lines of latitude are longer than those on the globe. The poles do not appear on this projection.

For azimuthal projections, imagine that the globe is resting on a piece of paper, touching it at one point. Away from this point, the projection becomes increasingly distorted. A third, conical, projection contains lines of latitude and longitude cast on a cone. Here the distortion increases away from the line of contact.

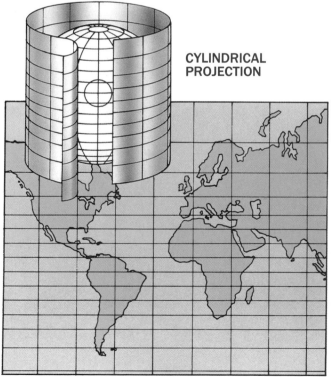

CYLINDRICAL PROJECTION

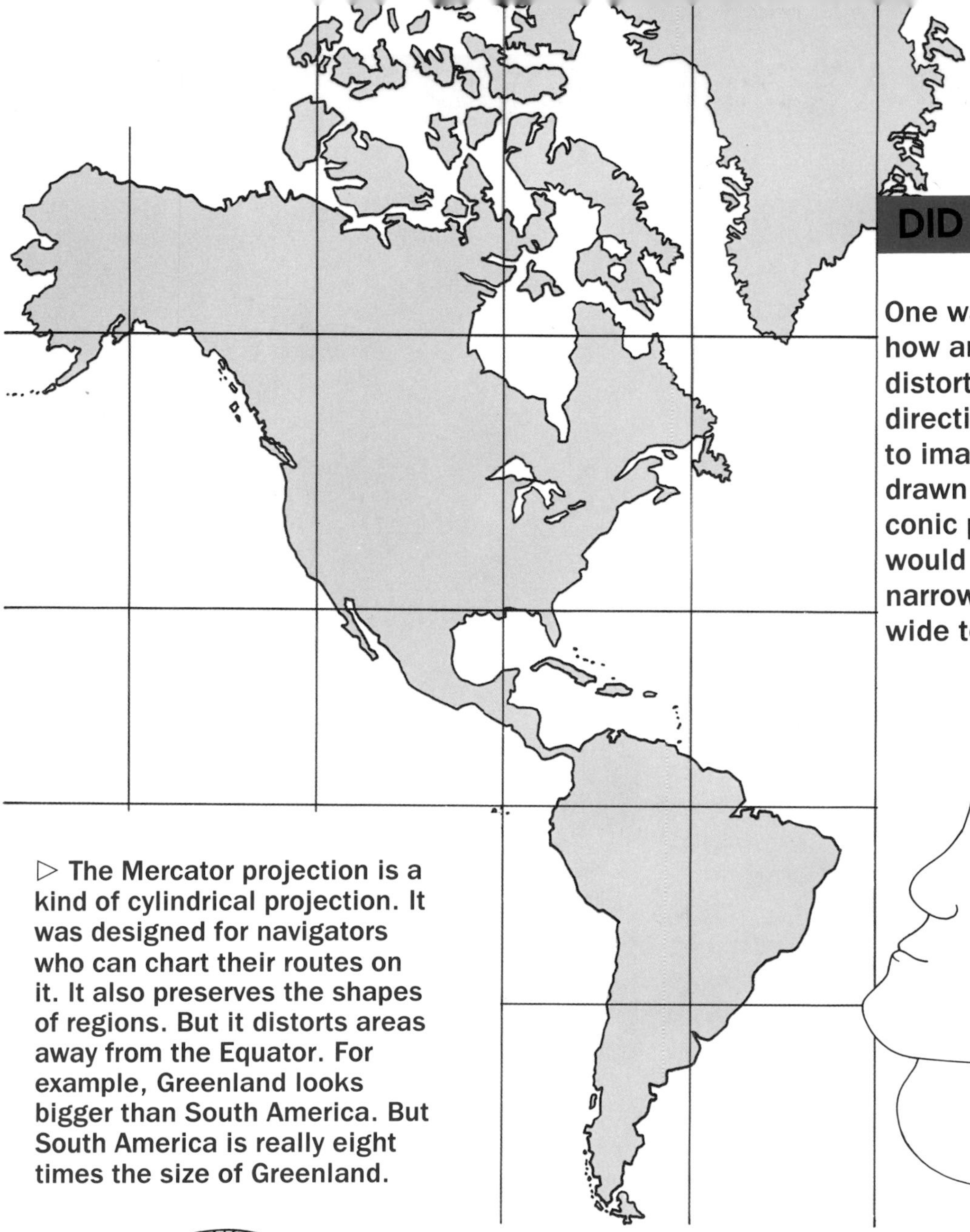

DID YOU KNOW?

One way of understanding how any map projection distorts shapes, areas, directions and distances is to imagine a human head drawn in the same way. On a conic projection, the head would be increasingly narrow towards the top and wide towards the bottom.

▷ The Mercator projection is a kind of cylindrical projection. It was designed for navigators who can chart their routes on it. It also preserves the shapes of regions. But it distorts areas away from the Equator. For example, Greenland looks bigger than South America. But South America is really eight times the size of Greenland.

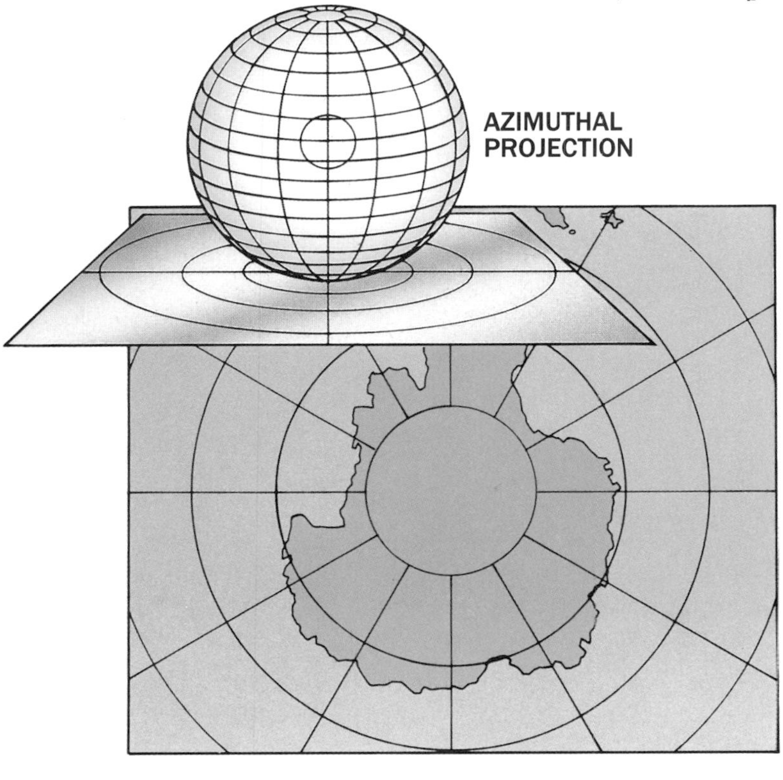

AZIMUTHAL
PROJECTION

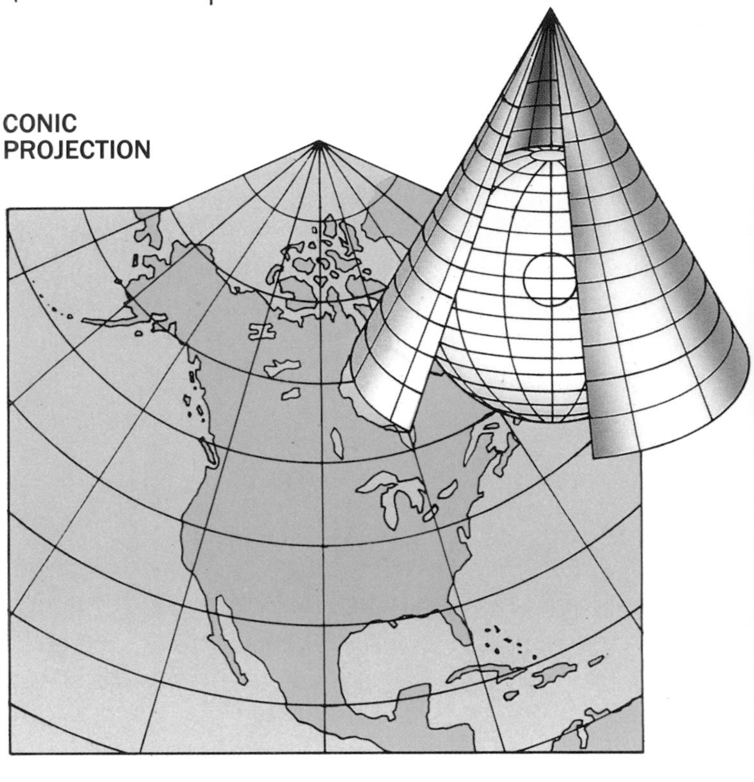

CONIC
PROJECTION

Navigators must have a good knowledge of maps and measurements. With maps and a compass, you can find your way across land areas. Ships' navigators use charts so that they can avoid dangerous reefs or sandbanks. Pilots of aircraft also use charts to plan their routes, which often follow great circles.

ALL AT SEA

An old method of navigation at sea was called dead reckoning. This involves recording the speed and direction of the ship. By noting the time, you can work out the distance you have travelled and mark your position on a chart. Navigators also work out their position by observing stars, using a sextant (to measure angles) and chronometers (extremely accurate clocks). The longitude is found by comparing the local time, measured from the positions of the Sun or stars, with Greenwich mean time.

Today, most navigators use electronic instruments. They include echo-sounders to find the depth of water, radio direction finders, radar and navigation satellites.

▷ Lighthouses warn sailors of rocky coasts, while radar helps pilots to locate coasts at night or in bad weather. Ships and aircraft use satellites to help them fix their positions.

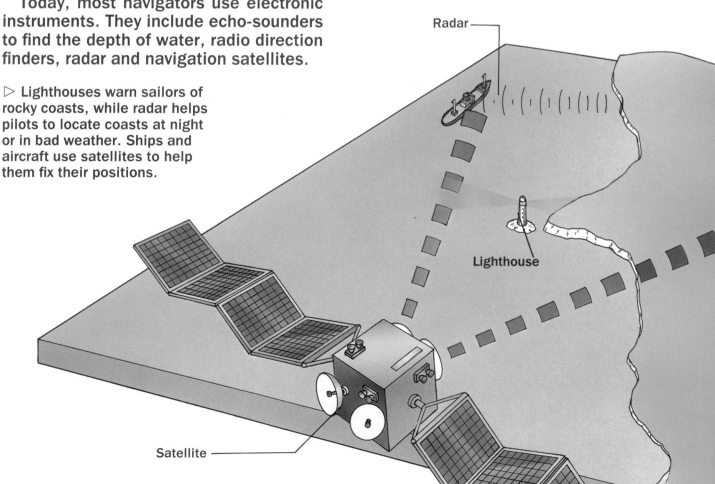

Radar

Lighthouse

Satellite

◁ Ships' navigators use a wide range of navigational instruments. In shallow waters, such as the estuaries (mouths) of rivers, ships take on pilots to guide them.

▽ Pilots of aircraft use Navigation Charts which show flight paths, notable landmarks, radio navigation stations and airports. This is a reduced example of a Navigation Chart.

IN THE AIR

Navigators on aircraft also use dead reckoning as well as navigating by the stars and the Sun. But much more important is electronic navigation. Radio direction finders enable navigators to obtain signals from known stations. By finding the direction to radio stations, they can check their own direction. Radar systems and signals from navigation satellites are used to help them fix their positions.

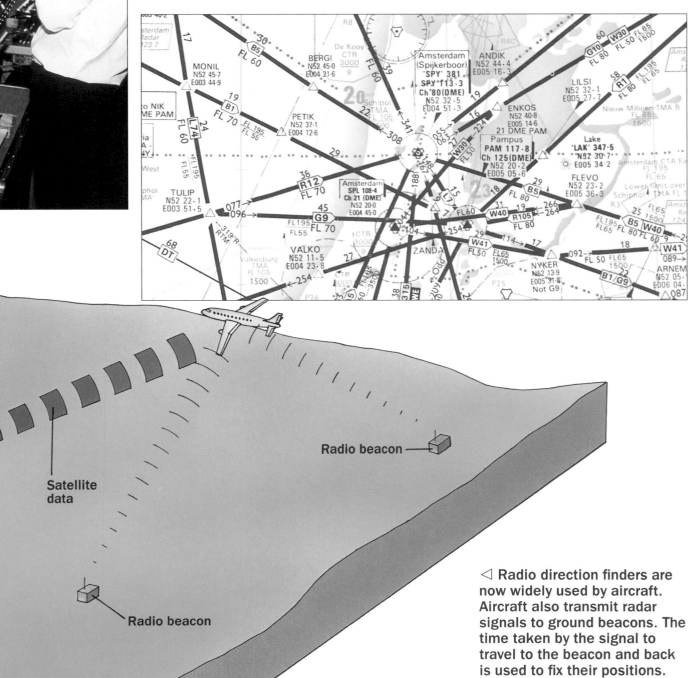

Satellite data

Radio beacon

Radio beacon

◁ Radio direction finders are now widely used by aircraft. Aircraft also transmit radar signals to ground beacons. The time taken by the signal to travel to the beacon and back is used to fix their positions.

The oldest known map is a clay tablet made in Babylonia (now in Iraq). Made in about 2250 BC, it shows a river flowing through a mountain valley. The ancient Egyptians used maps and calculated areas by using triangulation. Their work was developed by the ancient Greeks, who calculated the size of the Earth.

△ Ferdinand Magellan (1480-1521) led the first round-the-world voyage.

The first great map-maker was a Greek, Ptolemy, who lived between AD 100 and 165. He collected all the knowledge of his time in his book Geographia.

Christopher Columbus studied Ptolemy's maps before his voyage to the Americas in 1492. He accepted one of Ptolemy's mistakes, which suggested that the Earth is much smaller than it really is.

△ Lodestone, a magnetic rock, was used in early compasses.

In navigation, magnetic compasses were invented in China and the Mediterranean Sea region about 850 years ago. By the 1400s, sailors used charts to find their way around coasts. Sextants and chronometers came into use in the 1700s. The late 1900s has seen the development of electronic equipment in navigation and map-making.

▽ An early world map (1730).

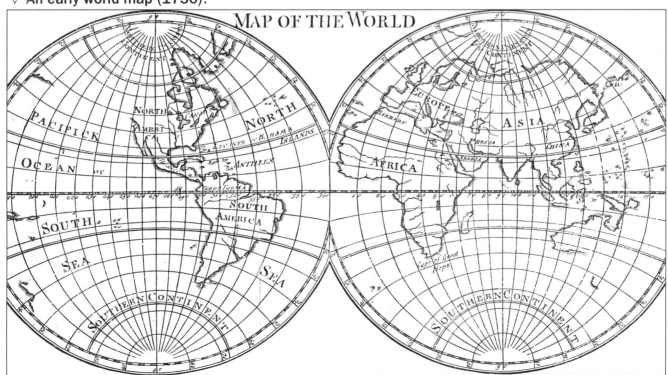

Axis
The line about which a body rotates. The Earth's axis, an imaginary line joining the North and South poles through the centre of the Earth, is tilted by 23.5 degrees.

Contour
A line on a map that joins places of equal height.

Control points
Places whose positions are fixed by measurement in the first stage of a survey.

General reference map
A map that shows general information, including natural and human features.

Graduated staff
A pole used in surveying. It has a scale, like a tall ruler, that indicates vertical heights.

Graticule
A network of lines of latitude and longitude on a map or globe.

Great circle
Any circle around the Earth that, if the Earth were cut through the line, divides the Earth into two equal parts. The shortest distance between any two points on the Earth's surface follows the path of a great circle.

Greenwich mean time (GMT)
The time at Greenwich, London, which lies on the prime meridian. Time zones are measured east and west of the prime meridian, just like degrees of longitude.

Grid
A framework of squares on a map which helps map-users to find the places they want on the map.

Latitude
On maps, the Equator and other lines parallel to it are lines of latitude, or parallels. They are stated in degrees from the centre of the Earth, from 0 degrees at the Equator to 90 degrees North at the North Pole and 90 degrees South at the South Pole.

Longitude
Lines of longitude, or meridians, run at right angles to lines of latitude. They all pass through the North and South Poles. Lines of longitude are measured 180 degrees East and West of the prime meridian (0 degrees longitude).

Magnetic poles
The Earth is like a giant magnet and it has a north and a south magnetic pole. The needles in magnetic compasses point to the north magnetic pole, which is near the true North Pole. The positions of the magnetic poles slowly change from time to time.

Prime meridian
The line of longitude (0 degrees) that runs from the North Pole, through Greenwich, London, to the South Pole.

Relief
Differences in the height of the land.

Topographic map
A map with a large enough scale to show the details of the land. Many governments publish a series of topographic maps of their countries at scales of around 1:50,000.

Triangulation
The method of measuring the land based on the principle that if you know the length of one side of a triangle and all three angles, then you can calculate the lengths of the other two sides. It is often used in map-making.

Photographic Credits:
Cover and pages 24-25 and 30 top right:
Science Photo Library; pages 5, 18-19,
22, 23 and 28: Frank Spooner Pictures;
page 6-7 all: Roger Vlitos; page 9 top:
The London Transport Museum; page 9
bottom, 30 top left and 30 bottom: Mary
Evans Picture Library; page 15: NASA;
page 16: Robert Harding Picture Library;
page 24 top: Aviation Picture Library;
page 29: Aerad Customer Services.